NETFLIX

STRANGER THINGS

Published by Danilo Promotions Ltd. Unit 3, The io Centre, Lea Road, Waltham Abbey, EN9 1AS, England.
Enquiries: **info@danilo.com** For all other information: **www.danilo.com**
Printed in China.

PERSONAL INFORMATION

Name:

Address:

Mobile:

Email:

IN CASE OF EMERGENCY PLEASE CONTACT

Name:

Address:

Mobile:

Doctor:

Doctor Telephone:

Known Allergies:

NOTES

Stranger Things

2023 YEAR TO VIEW

JANUARY

WK	M	T	W	T	F	S	S
52							1
1	2	3	4	5	6	7	8
2	9	10	11	12	13	14	15
3	16	17	18	19	20	21	22
4	23	24	25	26	27	28	29
5	30	31					

FEBRUARY

WK	M	T	W	T	F	S	S
5			1	2	3	4	5
6	6	7	8	9	10	11	12
7	13	14	15	16	17	18	19
8	20	21	22	23	24	25	26
9	27	28					

MARCH

WK	M	T	W	T	F	S	S
9			1	2	3	4	5
10	6	7	8	9	10	11	12
11	13	14	15	16	17	18	19
12	20	21	22	23	24	25	26
13	27	28	29	30	31		

APRIL

WK	M	T	W	T	F	S	S
13						1	2
14	3	4	5	6	7	8	9
15	10	11	12	13	14	15	16
16	17	18	19	20	21	22	23
17	24	25	26	27	28	29	30

MAY

WK	M	T	W	T	F	S	S
18	1	2	3	4	5	6	7
19	8	9	10	11	12	13	14
20	15	16	17	18	19	20	21
21	22	23	24	25	26	27	28
22	29	30	31				

JUNE

WK	M	T	W	T	F	S	S
22				1	2	3	4
23	5	6	7	8	9	10	11
24	12	13	14	15	16	17	18
25	19	20	21	22	23	24	25
26	26	27	28	29	30		

JULY

WK	M	T	W	T	F	S	S
26						1	2
27	3	4	5	6	7	8	9
28	10	11	12	13	14	15	16
29	17	18	19	20	21	22	23
30	24	25	26	27	28	29	30
31	31						

AUGUST

WK	M	T	W	T	F	S	S
31		1	2	3	4	5	6
32	7	8	9	10	11	12	13
33	14	15	16	17	18	19	20
34	21	22	23	24	25	26	27
35	28	29	30	31			

SEPTEMBER

WK	M	T	W	T	F	S	S
35					1	2	3
36	4	5	6	7	8	9	10
37	11	12	13	14	15	16	17
38	18	19	20	21	22	23	24
39	25	26	27	28	29	30	

OCTOBER

WK	M	T	W	T	F	S	S
39							1
40	2	3	4	5	6	7	8
41	9	10	11	12	13	14	15
42	16	17	18	19	20	21	22
43	23	24	25	26	27	28	29
44	30	31					

NOVEMBER

WK	M	T	W	T	F	S	S
44			1	2	3	4	5
45	6	7	8	9	10	11	12
46	13	14	15	16	17	18	19
47	20	21	22	23	24	25	26
48	27	28	29	30			

DECEMBER

WK	M	T	W	T	F	S	S
48					1	2	3
49	4	5	6	7	8	9	10
50	11	12	13	14	15	16	17
51	18	19	20	21	22	23	24
52	25	26	27	28	29	30	31

2024 YEAR TO VIEW

JANUARY

WK	M	T	W	T	F	S	S
1	1	2	3	4	5	6	7
2	8	9	10	11	12	13	14
3	15	16	17	18	19	20	21
4	22	23	24	25	26	27	28
5	29	30	31				

FEBRUARY

WK	M	T	W	T	F	S	S
5				1	2	3	4
6	5	6	7	8	9	10	11
7	12	13	14	15	16	17	18
8	19	20	21	22	23	24	25
9	26	27	28	29			

MARCH

WK	M	T	W	T	F	S	S
9					1	2	3
10	4	5	6	7	8	9	10
11	11	12	13	14	15	16	17
12	18	19	20	21	22	23	24
13	25	26	27	28	29	30	31

APRIL

WK	M	T	W	T	F	S	S
14	1	2	3	4	5	6	7
15	8	9	10	11	12	13	14
16	15	16	17	18	19	20	21
17	22	23	24	25	26	27	28
18	29	30					

MAY

WK	M	T	W	T	F	S	S
18			1	2	3	4	5
19	6	7	8	9	10	11	12
20	13	14	15	16	17	18	19
21	20	21	22	23	24	25	26
22	27	28	29	30	31		

JUNE

WK	M	T	W	T	F	S	S
22						1	2
23	3	4	5	6	7	8	9
24	10	11	12	13	14	15	16
25	17	18	19	20	21	22	23
26	24	25	26	27	28	29	30

JULY

WK	M	T	W	T	F	S	S
27	1	2	3	4	5	6	7
28	8	9	10	11	12	13	14
29	15	16	17	18	19	20	21
30	22	23	24	25	26	27	28
31	29	30	31				

AUGUST

WK	M	T	W	T	F	S	S
31				1	2	3	4
32	5	6	7	8	9	10	11
33	12	13	14	15	16	17	18
34	19	20	21	22	23	24	25
35	26	27	28	29	30	31	

SEPTEMBER

WK	M	T	W	T	F	S	S
35							1
36	2	3	4	5	6	7	8
37	9	10	11	12	13	14	15
38	16	17	18	19	20	21	22
39	23	24	25	26	27	28	29
40	30						

OCTOBER

WK	M	T	W	T	F	S	S
40		1	2	3	4	5	6
41	7	8	9	10	11	12	13
42	14	15	16	17	18	19	20
43	21	22	23	24	25	26	27
44	28	29	30	31			

NOVEMBER

WK	M	T	W	T	F	S	S
44					1	2	3
45	4	5	6	7	8	9	10
46	11	12	13	14	15	16	17
47	18	19	20	21	22	23	24
48	25	26	27	28	29	30	

DECEMBER

WK	M	T	W	T	F	S	S
48							1
49	2	3	4	5	6	7	8
50	9	10	11	12	13	14	15
51	16	17	18	19	20	21	22
52	23	24	25	26	27	28	29
1	30	31					

2023 NOTABLE DATES

	2023
New Year's Day	JAN 1
New Year Holiday	JAN 2
Bank Holiday (Scotland)	JAN 3
Chinese New Year (Rabbit)	JAN 22
Valentine's Day	FEB 14
Shrove Tuesday	FEB 21
St. David's Day	MAR 1
St. Patrick's Day	MAR 17
Mothering Sunday (UK)	MAR 19
Ramadan Begins	MAR 22
Daylight Saving Time Starts	MAR 26
Passover Begins	APR 5
Good Friday	APR 7
Easter Sunday	APR 9
Easter Monday	APR 10
Earth Day	APR 22
St. George's Day	APR 23
Early May Bank Holiday	MAY 1
Spring Bank Holiday	MAY 29
Father's Day (UK)	JUN 18
Public Holiday (Northern Ireland)	JUL 12
Islamic New Year Begins	JUL 18
Summer Bank Holiday (Scotland)	AUG 7
Summer Bank Holiday (ENG, NIR, WAL)	AUG 28
Rosh Hashanah (Jewish New Year) Begins	SEP 15
International Day of Peace (United Nations)	SEP 21
Yom Kippur Begins	SEP 24
World Mental Health Day	OCT 10
Daylight Saving Time Ends	OCT 29
Halloween	OCT 31
Guy Fawkes Night	NOV 5
Diwali / Remembrance Sunday	NOV 12
St. Andrew's Day	NOV 30
Christmas Day	DEC 25
Boxing Day	DEC 26
New Year's Eve	DEC 31

PLANNER 2023

JANUARY		FEBRUARY		MARCH	
1	S	1	W	1	W
2	M	2	T	2	T
3	T	3	F	3	F
4	W	4	S	4	S
5	T	5	S	5	S
6	F	6	M	6	M
7	S	7	T	7	T
8	S	8	W	8	W
9	M	9	T	9	T
10	T	10	F	10	F
11	W	11	S	11	S
12	T	12	S	12	S
13	F	13	M	13	M
14	S	14	T	14	T
15	S	15	W	15	W
16	M	16	T	16	T
17	T	17	F	17	F
18	W	18	S	18	S
19	T	19	S	19	S
20	F	20	M	20	M
21	S	21	T	21	T
22	S	22	W	22	W
23	M	23	T	23	T
24	T	24	F	24	F
25	W	25	S	25	S
26	T	26	S	26	S
27	F	27	M	27	M
28	S	28	T	28	T
29	S			29	W
30	M			30	T
31	T			31	F

APRIL

1 S
2 S
3 M
4 T
5 W
6 T
7 F
8 S
9 S
10 M
11 T
12 W
13 T
14 F
15 S
16 S
17 M
18 T
19 W
20 T
21 F
22 S
23 S
24 M
25 T
26 W
27 T
28 F
29 S
30 S

MAY

1 M
2 T
3 W
4 T
5 F
6 S
7 S
8 M
9 T
10 W
11 T
12 F
13 S
14 S
15 M
16 T
17 W
18 T
19 F
20 S
21 S
22 M
23 T
24 W
25 T
26 F
27 S
28 S
29 M
30 T
31 W

JUNE

1 T
2 F
3 S
4 S
5 M
6 T
7 W
8 T
9 F
10 S
11 S
12 M
13 T
14 W
15 T
16 F
17 S
18 S
19 M
20 T
21 W
22 T
23 F
24 S
25 S
26 M
27 T
28 W
29 T
30 F

PLANNER 2023

JULY	AUGUST	SEPTEMBER
1 S	1 T	1 F
2 S	2 W	2 S
3 M	3 T	3 S
4 T	4 F	4 M
5 W	5 S	5 T
6 T	6 S	6 W
7 F	7 M	7 T
8 S	8 T	8 F
9 S	9 W	9 S
10 M	10 T	10 S
11 T	11 F	11 M
12 W	12 S	12 T
13 T	13 S	13 W
14 F	14 M	14 T
15 S	15 T	15 F
16 S	16 W	16 S
17 M	17 T	17 S
18 T	18 F	18 M
19 W	19 S	19 T
20 T	20 S	20 W
21 F	21 M	21 T
22 S	22 T	22 F
23 S	23 W	23 S
24 M	24 T	24 S
25 T	25 F	25 M
26 W	26 S	26 T
27 T	27 S	27 W
28 F	28 M	28 T
29 S	29 T	29 F
30 S	30 W	30 S
31 M	31 T	

OCTOBER	NOVEMBER	DECEMBER
1 S	1 W	1 F
2 M	2 T	2 S
3 T	3 F	3 S
4 W	4 S	4 M
5 T	5 S	5 T
6 F	6 M	6 W
7 S	7 T	7 T
8 S	8 W	8 F
9 M	9 T	9 S
10 T	10 F	10 S
11 W	11 S	11 M
12 T	12 S	12 T
13 F	13 M	13 W
14 S	14 T	14 T
15 S	15 W	15 F
16 M	16 T	16 S
17 T	17 F	17 S
18 W	18 S	18 M
19 T	19 S	19 T
20 F	20 M	20 W
21 S	21 T	21 T
22 S	22 W	22 F
23 M	23 T	23 S
24 T	24 F	24 S
25 W	25 S	25 M
26 T	26 S	26 T
27 F	27 M	27 W
28 S	28 T	28 T
29 S	29 W	29 F
30 M	30 T	30 S
31 T		31 S

WE'VE GOT
A CODE RED!
Lucas

JANUARY

NOTES

ST

26 MONDAY

27 TUESDAY

28 WEDNESDAY

29 THURSDAY

J

FRIDAY 30

New Year's Eve

SATURDAY 31

New Year's Day

SUNDAY 1

NOTES

STRANGER THINGS

T	F	S	S	M	T	W	T	F	S	S	M	T	W	T	F	S	S	M	T	W	T	F	S	S	M	T	W	T	F	S
15	16	17	18	19	20	21	22	23	24	25	26	27	28	29	30	31	1	2	3	4	5	6	7	8	9	10	11	12	13	14

2 MONDAY

New Year Holiday

3 TUESDAY

Bank Holiday (Scotland)

4 WEDNESDAY

5 THURSDAY

FRIDAY 6

SATURDAY 7

SUNDAY 8

NOTES

STRANGER THINGS

S	M	T	W	T	F	S	S	M	T	W	T	F	S	S	M	T	W	T	F	S	S	M	T	W	T	F	S	S	M	T
1	2	3	4	5	6	7	8	9	10	11	12	13	14	15	16	17	18	19	20	21	22	23	24	25	26	27	28	29	30	31

9 MONDAY

10 TUESDAY

11 WEDNESDAY

12 THURSDAY

FRIDAY 13

SATURDAY 14

SUNDAY 15

NOTES

S	M	T	W	T	F	S	S	M	T	W	T	F	S	S	M	T	W	T	F	S	S	M	T	W	T	F	S	S	M	T
1	2	3	4	5	6	7	8	9	10	11	12	13	14	15	16	17	18	19	20	21	22	23	24	25	26	27	28	29	30	31

16 MONDAY

17 TUESDAY

18 WEDNESDAY

19 THURSDAY

FRIDAY 20

SATURDAY 21

Chinese New Year (Rabbit)

SUNDAY 22

NOTES

S	M	T	W	T	F	S	S	M	T	W	T	F	S	S	M	T	W	T	F	S	S	M	T	W	T	F	S	S	M	T
1	2	3	4	5	6	7	8	9	10	11	12	13	14	15	16	17	18	19	20	21	22	23	24	25	26	27	28	29	30	31

23 MONDAY

24 TUESDAY

25 WEDNESDAY

26 THURSDAY

FRIDAY 27

SATURDAY 28

SUNDAY 29

NOTES

S	M	T	W	T	F	S	S	M	T	W	T	F	S	S	M	T	W	T	F	S	S	M	T	W	T	F	S	S	M	T
1	2	3	4	5	6	7	8	9	10	11	12	13	14	15	16	17	18	19	20	21	22	23	24	25	26	27	28	29	30	31

BECAUSE SEE,
WITHOUT HEART
WE'D ALL
FALL APART
Will

FEBRUARY

NOTES

Greetings from the UPSIDE DOWN

30 MONDAY

31 TUESDAY

1 WEDNESDAY

2 THURSDAY

F

FRIDAY 3

SATURDAY 4

SUNDAY 5

NOTES

STRANGER THINGS

M	T	W	T	F	S	S	M	T	W	T	F	S	S	M	T	W	T	F	S	S	M	T	W	T	F	S	S	M	T	W
16	17	18	19	20	21	22	23	24	25	26	27	28	29	30	31	1	2	3	4	5	6	7	8	9	10	11	12	13	14	15

6 MONDAY

7 TUESDAY

8 WEDNESDAY

9 THURSDAY

FRIDAY 10

SATURDAY 11

SUNDAY 12

NOTES

W	T	F	S	S	M	T	W	T	F	S	S	M	T	W	T	F	S	S	M	T	W	T	F	S	S	M	T
1	2	3	4	5	6	7	8	9	10	11	12	13	14	15	16	17	18	19	20	21	22	23	24	25	26	27	28

13 MONDAY

14 TUESDAY

Valentine's Day

15 WEDNESDAY

16 THURSDAY

FRIDAY 17

SATURDAY 18

SUNDAY 19

NOTES

W	T	F	S	S	M	T	W	T	F	S	S	M	T	W	T	F	S	S	M	T	W	T	F	S	S	M	T
1	2	3	4	5	6	7	8	9	10	11	12	13	14	15	16	17	18	19	20	21	22	23	24	25	26	27	28

20 MONDAY

21 TUESDAY

Shrove Tuesday

22 WEDNESDAY

23 THURSDAY

FRIDAY 24

SATURDAY 25

SUNDAY 26

NOTES

W	T	F	S	S	M	T	W	T	F	S	S	M	T	W	T	F	S	S	M	T	W	T	F	S	S	M	T
1	2	3	4	5	6	7	8	9	10	11	12	13	14	15	16	17	18	19	20	21	22	23	24	25	26	27	28

PLATONIC
WITH A
CAPITAL P
Steve

MARCH

NOTES

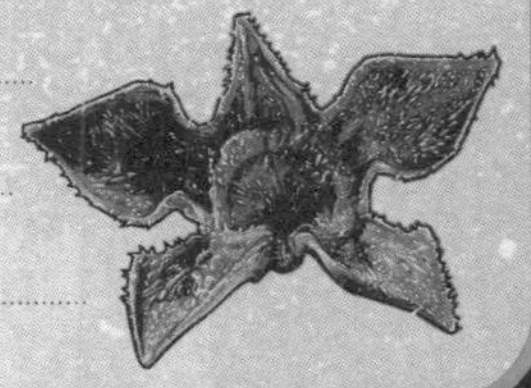

27 MONDAY

28 TUESDAY

1 WEDNESDAY

St. David's Day

2 THURSDAY

FRIDAY 3

SATURDAY 4

SUNDAY 5

NOTES

STRANGER THINGS

W	T	F	S	S	M	T	W	T	F	S	S	M	T	W	T	F	S	S	M	T	W	T	F	S	S	M	T
15	16	17	18	19	20	21	22	23	24	25	26	27	28	1	2	3	4	5	6	7	8	9	10	11	12	13	14

6 MONDAY

7 TUESDAY

8 WEDNESDAY

9 THURSDAY

FRIDAY 10

SATURDAY 11

SUNDAY 12

NOTES

STRANGER THINGS

W	T	F	S	S	M	T	W	T	F	S	S	M	T	W	T	F	S	S	M	T	W	T	F	S	S	M	T	W	T	F
1	2	3	4	5	6	7	8	9	10	11	12	13	14	15	16	17	18	19	20	21	22	23	24	25	26	27	28	29	30	31

13 MONDAY

14 TUESDAY

15 WEDNESDAY

16 THURSDAY

FRIDAY 17

St. Patrick's Day

SATURDAY 18

SUNDAY 19

Mothering Sunday (UK)

NOTES

STRANGER THINGS

W	T	F	S	S	M	T	W	T	F	S	S	M	T	W	T	F	S	S	M	T	W	T	F	S	S	M	T	W	T	F
1	2	3	4	5	6	7	8	9	10	11	12	13	14	15	16	17	18	19	20	21	22	23	24	25	26	27	28	29	30	31

20 MONDAY

21 TUESDAY

22 WEDNESDAY

Ramadan Begins

23 THURSDAY

FRIDAY 24

SATURDAY 25

SUNDAY 26

Daylight Saving Time Starts

NOTES

STRANGER THINGS

W	T	F	S	S	M	T	W	T	F	S	S	M	T	W	T	F	S	S	M	T	W	T	F	S	S	M	T	W	T	F
1	2	3	4	5	6	7	8	9	10	11	12	13	14	15	16	17	18	19	20	21	22	23	24	25	26	27	28	29	30	31

M

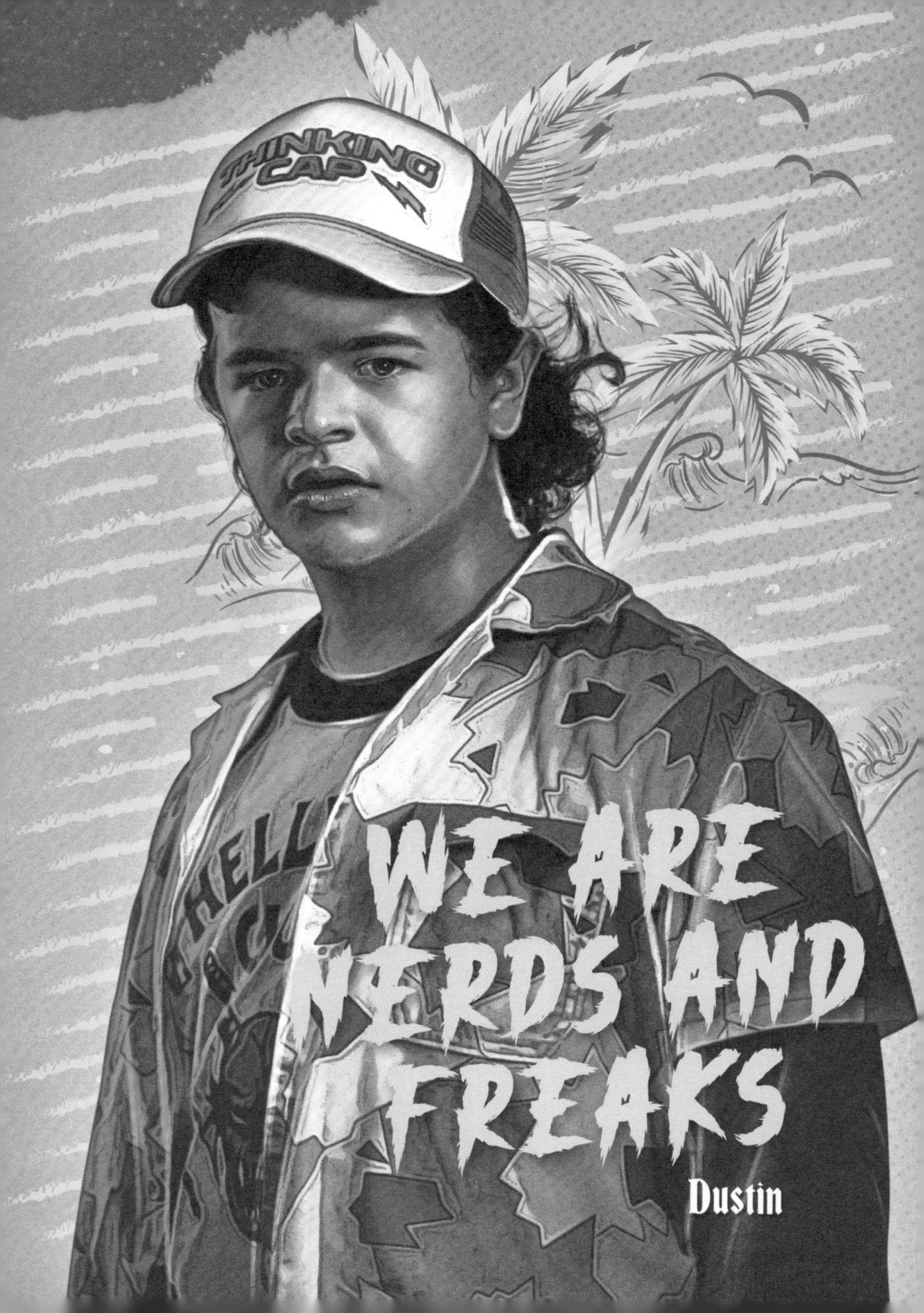
THINKING CAP
WE ARE NERDS AND FREAKS
Dustin

APRIL

NOTES

Stranger Things

27 MONDAY

28 TUESDAY

29 WEDNESDAY

30 THURSDAY

FRIDAY 31

SATURDAY 1

SUNDAY 2

T	F	S	S	M	T	W	T	F	S	S	M	T	W	T	F	S	S	M	T	W	T	F	S	S	M	T	W	T	F	S
16	17	18	19	20	21	22	23	24	25	26	27	28	29	30	31	1	2	3	4	5	6	7	8	9	10	11	12	13	14	15

3 MONDAY

4 TUESDAY

5 WEDNESDAY

Passover Begins

6 THURSDAY

Good Friday

FRIDAY 7

SATURDAY 8

Easter Sunday

SUNDAY 9

NOTES

STRANGER THINGS

S	S	M	T	W	T	F	S	S	M	T	W	T	F	S	S	M	T	W	T	F	S	S	M	T	W	T	F	S	S
1	2	3	4	5	6	7	8	9	10	11	12	13	14	15	16	17	18	19	20	21	22	23	24	25	26	27	28	29	30

10 MONDAY

Easter Monday

11 TUESDAY

12 WEDNESDAY

13 THURSDAY

FRIDAY 14

SATURDAY 15

SUNDAY 16

NOTES

STRANGER THINGS

S	S	M	T	W	T	F	S	S	M	T	W	T	F	S	S	M	T	W	T	F	S	S	M	T	W	T	F	S	S
1	2	3	4	5	6	7	8	9	10	11	12	13	14	15	16	17	18	19	20	21	22	23	24	25	26	27	28	29	30

17 MONDAY

18 TUESDAY

19 WEDNESDAY

20 THURSDAY

FRIDAY 21

Earth Day

SATURDAY 22

St. George's Day

SUNDAY 23

NOTES

STRANGER THINGS

S	S	M	T	W	T	F	S	S	M	T	W	T	F	S	S	M	T	W	T	F	S	S	M	T	W	T	F	S	S
1	2	3	4	5	6	7	8	9	10	11	12	13	14	15	16	17	18	19	20	21	22	23	24	25	26	27	28	29	30

24 MONDAY

25 TUESDAY

26 WEDNESDAY

27 THURSDAY

FRIDAY 28

SATURDAY 29

SUNDAY 30

NOTES

STRANGER THINGS

S	S	M	T	W	T	F	S	S	M	T	W	T	F	S	S	M	T	W	T	F	S	S	M	T	W	T	F	S	S
1	2	3	4	5	6	7	8	9	10	11	12	13	14	15	16	17	18	19	20	21	22	23	24	25	26	27	28	29	30

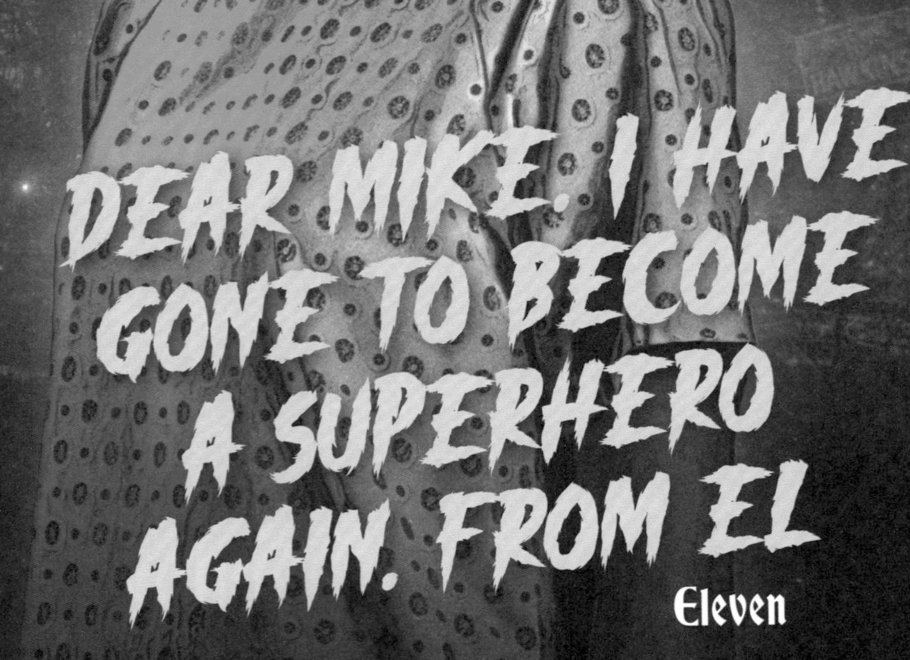
DEAR MIKE. I HAVE
GONE TO BECOME
A SUPERHERO
AGAIN. FROM EL
Eleven

MAY

NOTES

ST

1 MONDAY

Early May Bank Holiday

2 TUESDAY

3 WEDNESDAY

4 THURSDAY

FRIDAY 5

SATURDAY 6

SUNDAY 7

NOTES

STRANGER THINGS

M	T	W	T	F	S	S	M	T	W	T	F	S	S	M	T	W	T	F	S	S	M	T	W	T	F	S	S	M	T	W
1	2	3	4	5	6	7	8	9	10	11	12	13	14	15	16	17	18	19	20	21	22	23	24	25	26	27	28	29	30	31

8 MONDAY

9 TUESDAY

10 WEDNESDAY

11 THURSDAY

FRIDAY 12

SATURDAY 13

M

SUNDAY 14

NOTES

STRANGER THINGS

M	T	W	T	F	S	S	M	T	W	T	F	S	S	M	T	W	T	F	S	S	M	T	W	T	F	S	S	M	T	W
1	2	3	4	5	6	7	8	9	10	11	12	13	14	15	16	17	18	19	20	21	22	23	24	25	26	27	28	29	30	31

15 MONDAY

16 TUESDAY

17 WEDNESDAY

18 THURSDAY

FRIDAY 19

SATURDAY 20

M

SUNDAY 21

NOTES

STRANGER THINGS

M	T	W	T	F	S	S	M	T	W	T	F	S	S	M	T	W	T	F	S	S	M	T	W	T	F	S	S	M	T	W
1	2	3	4	5	6	7	8	9	10	11	12	13	14	15	16	17	18	19	20	21	22	23	24	25	26	27	28	29	30	31

22 MONDAY

23 TUESDAY

24 WEDNESDAY

25 THURSDAY

FRIDAY 26

SATURDAY 27

M

SUNDAY 28

NOTES

M	T	W	T	F	S	S	M	T	W	T	F	S	S	M	T	W	T	F	S	S	M	T	W	T	F	S	S	M	T	W
1	2	3	4	5	6	7	8	9	10	11	12	13	14	15	16	17	18	19	20	21	22	23	24	25	26	27	28	29	30	31

BUCKLE UP, MY THREE AMIGOS!
Argyle

JUNE

NOTES

Surfer Boy Pizza
pizza
Surfer Boy
TELEPHONE:
805-45-PIZZA
HOT TO YOUR DOOR

29 MONDAY

Spring Bank Holiday

30 TUESDAY

31 WEDNESDAY

1 THURSDAY

FRIDAY 2

SATURDAY 3

SUNDAY 4

NOTES

STRANGER THINGS

T	W	T	F	S	S	M	T	W	T	F	S	S	M	T	W	T	F	S	S	M	T	W	T	F	S	S	M	T	W	T
16	17	18	19	20	21	22	23	24	25	26	27	28	29	30	31	1	2	3	4	5	6	7	8	9	10	11	12	13	14	15

5 MONDAY

6 TUESDAY

7 WEDNESDAY

8 THURSDAY

FRIDAY 9

SATURDAY 10

SUNDAY 11

NOTES

STRANGER THINGS

T	F	S	S	M	T	W	T	F	S	S	M	T	W	T	F	S	S	M	T	W	T	F	S	S	M	T	W	T	F
1	2	3	4	5	6	7	8	9	10	11	12	13	14	15	16	17	18	19	20	21	22	23	24	25	26	27	28	29	30

12 MONDAY

13 TUESDAY

14 WEDNESDAY

15 THURSDAY

FRIDAY 16

SATURDAY 17

SUNDAY 18

Father's Day (UK)

NOTES

STRANGER THINGS

T	F	S	S	M	T	W	T	F	S	S	M	T	W	T	F	S	S	M	T	W	T	F	S	S	M	T	W	T	F
1	2	3	4	5	6	7	8	9	10	11	12	13	14	15	16	17	18	19	20	21	22	23	24	25	26	27	28	29	30

19 MONDAY

20 TUESDAY

21 WEDNESDAY

22 THURSDAY

FRIDAY 23

SATURDAY 24

SUNDAY 25

NOTES

T	F	S	S	M	T	W	T	F	S	S	M	T	W	T	F	S	S	M	T	W	T	F	S	S	M	T	W	T	F
1	2	3	4	5	6	7	8	9	10	11	12	13	14	15	16	17	18	19	20	21	22	23	24	25	26	27	28	29	30

J

I HATE
HIGH SCHOOL
Mike

JULY

NOTES

26 MONDAY

27 TUESDAY

28 WEDNESDAY

29 THURSDAY

FRIDAY 30

SATURDAY 1

SUNDAY 2

NOTES

STRANGER THINGS

F	S	S	M	T	W	T	F	S	S	M	T	W	T	F	S	S	M	T	W	T	F	S	S	M	T	W	T	F	S
16	17	18	19	20	21	22	23	24	25	26	27	28	29	30	1	2	3	4	5	6	7	8	9	10	11	12	13	14	15

3 MONDAY

4 TUESDAY

5 WEDNESDAY

6 THURSDAY

FRIDAY 7

SATURDAY 8

SUNDAY 9

NOTES

STRANGER THINGS

S	S	M	T	W	T	F	S	S	M	T	W	T	F	S	S	M	T	W	T	F	S	S	M	T	W	T	F	S	S	M
1	2	3	4	5	6	7	8	9	10	11	12	13	14	15	16	17	18	19	20	21	22	23	24	25	26	27	28	29	30	31

10 MONDAY

11 TUESDAY

12 WEDNESDAY

Public Holiday (Northern Ireland)

13 THURSDAY

FRIDAY 14

SATURDAY 15

SUNDAY 16

NOTES

S	S	M	T	W	T	F	S	S	M	T	W	T	F	S	S	M	T	W	T	F	S	S	M	T	W	T	F	S	S	M
1	2	3	4	5	6	7	8	9	10	11	12	13	14	15	16	17	18	19	20	21	22	23	24	25	26	27	28	29	30	31

17 MONDAY

18 TUESDAY

Islamic New Year Begins

19 WEDNESDAY

20 THURSDAY

FRIDAY 21

SATURDAY 22

SUNDAY 23

NOTES

S	S	M	T	W	T	F	S	S	M	T	W	T	F	S	S	M	T	W	T	F	S	S	M	T	W	T	F	S	S	M
1	2	3	4	5	6	7	8	9	10	11	12	13	14	15	16	17	18	19	20	21	22	23	24	25	26	27	28	29	30	31

24 MONDAY

25 TUESDAY

26 WEDNESDAY

27 THURSDAY

FRIDAY **28**

SATURDAY **29**

SUNDAY **30**

NOTES

STRANGER THINGS

S	S	M	T	W	T	F	S	S	M	T	W	T	F	S	S	M	T	W	T	F	S	S	M	T	W	T	F	S	S	M
1	2	3	4	5	6	7	8	9	10	11	12	13	14	15	16	17	18	19	20	21	22	23	24	25	26	27	28	29	30	31

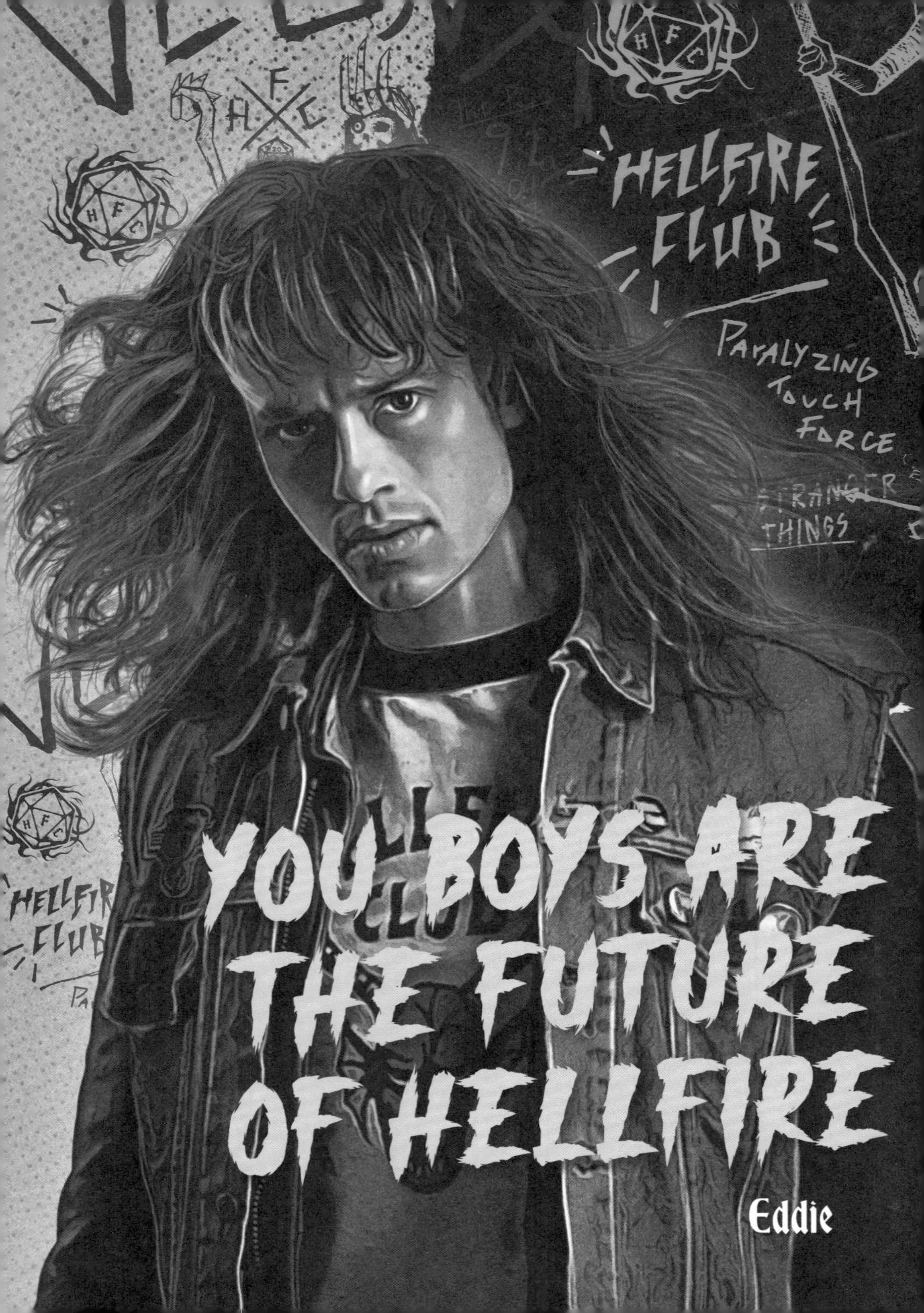
HELLFIRE
CLUB
PARALYZING
TOUCH
FORCE
STRANGER
THINGS
HELLFIRE
CLUB
YOU BOYS ARE
THE FUTURE
OF HELLFIRE
Eddie

AUGUST

NOTES

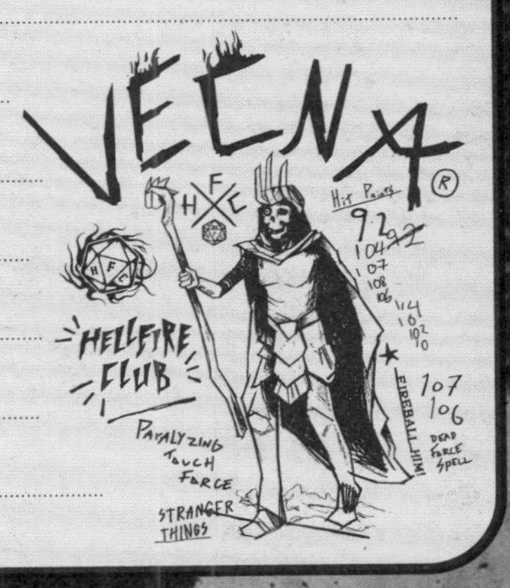

31 MONDAY

1 TUESDAY

2 WEDNESDAY

3 THURSDAY

FRIDAY 4

SATURDAY 5

SUNDAY 6

A

NOTES

STRANGER THINGS

S	M	T	W	T	F	S	S	M	T	W	T	F	S	S	M	T	W	T	F	S	S	M	T	W	T	F	S	S	M	T
16	17	18	19	20	21	22	23	24	25	26	27	28	29	30	31	1	2	3	4	5	6	7	8	9	10	11	12	13	14	15

7 MONDAY

Summer Bank Holiday (Scotland)

8 TUESDAY

9 WEDNESDAY

10 THURSDAY

FRIDAY 11

SATURDAY 12

SUNDAY 13

A

NOTES

STRANGER THINGS

T	W	T	F	S	S	M	T	W	T	F	S	S	M	T	W	T	F	S	S	M	T	W	T	F	S	S	M	T	W	T
1	2	3	4	5	6	7	8	9	10	11	12	13	14	15	16	17	18	19	20	21	22	23	24	25	26	27	28	29	30	31

14 MONDAY

15 TUESDAY

16 WEDNESDAY

17 THURSDAY

FRIDAY 18

SATURDAY 19

SUNDAY 20

NOTES

T	W	T	F	S	S	M	T	W	T	F	S	S	M	T	W	T	F	S	S	M	T	W	T	F	S	S	M	T	W	T
1	2	3	4	5	6	7	8	9	10	11	12	13	14	15	16	17	18	19	20	21	22	23	24	25	26	27	28	29	30	31

A

21 MONDAY

22 TUESDAY

23 WEDNESDAY

24 THURSDAY

FRIDAY 25

SATURDAY 26

SUNDAY 27

A

NOTES

T	W	T	F	S	S	M	T	W	T	F	S	S	M	T	W	T	F	S	S	M	T	W	T	F	S	S	M	T	W	T
1	2	3	4	5	6	7	8	9	10	11	12	13	14	15	16	17	18	19	20	21	22	23	24	25	26	27	28	29	30	31

HELLFIRE'S NOT A CULT – IT'S A CLUB FOR NERDS!

Erica

SEPTEMBER

NOTES

28 MONDAY

Summer Bank Holiday (ENG, NIR, WAL)

29 TUESDAY

30 WEDNESDAY

31 THURSDAY

FRIDAY 1

SATURDAY 2

SUNDAY 3

5

NOTES

STRANGER THINGS

W	T	F	S	S	M	T	W	T	F	S	S	M	T	W	T	F	S	S	M	T	W	T	F	S	S	M	T	W	T	F
16	17	18	19	20	21	22	23	24	25	26	27	28	29	30	31	1	2	3	4	5	6	7	8	9	10	11	12	13	14	15

4 MONDAY

5 TUESDAY

6 WEDNESDAY

7 THURSDAY

FRIDAY 8

SATURDAY 9

SUNDAY 10

NOTES

STRANGER THINGS

F	S	S	M	T	W	T	F	S	S	M	T	W	T	F	S	S	M	T	W	T	F	S	S	M	T	W	T	F	S
1	2	3	4	5	6	7	8	9	10	11	12	13	14	15	16	17	18	19	20	21	22	23	24	25	26	27	28	29	30

11 MONDAY

12 TUESDAY

13 WEDNESDAY

14 THURSDAY

FRIDAY 15

Rosh Hashanah [Jewish New Year] Begins

SATURDAY 16

SUNDAY 17

NOTES

STRANGER THINGS

F	S	S	M	T	W	T	F	S	S	M	T	W	T	F	S	S	M	T	W	T	F	S	S	M	T	W	T	F	S
1	2	3	4	5	6	7	8	9	10	11	12	13	14	15	16	17	18	19	20	21	22	23	24	25	26	27	28	29	30

18 MONDAY

19 TUESDAY

20 WEDNESDAY

21 THURSDAY

International Day of Peace (United Nations)

FRIDAY 22

SATURDAY 23

SUNDAY 24

Yom Kippur Begins

NOTES

STRANGER THINGS

F	S	S	M	T	W	T	F	S	S	M	T	W	T	F	S	S	M	T	W	T	F	S	S	M	T	W	T	F	S
1	2	3	4	5	6	7	8	9	10	11	12	13	14	15	16	17	18	19	20	21	22	23	24	25	26	27	28	29	30

WE'VE
GOT THIS
Robin

OCTOBER

NOTES

Stranger Things

25 MONDAY

26 TUESDAY

27 WEDNESDAY

28 THURSDAY

FRIDAY 29

SATURDAY 30

SUNDAY 1

NOTES

S	S	M	T	W	T	F	S	S	M	T	W	T	F	S	S	M	T	W	T	F	S	S	M	T	W	T	F	S	S
16	17	18	19	20	21	22	23	24	25	26	27	28	29	30	1	2	3	4	5	6	7	8	9	10	11	12	13	14	15

2 MONDAY

3 TUESDAY

4 WEDNESDAY

5 THURSDAY

FRIDAY 6

SATURDAY 7

SUNDAY 8

NOTES

STRANGER THINGS

S	M	T	W	T	F	S	S	M	T	W	T	F	S	S	M	T	W	T	F	S	S	M	T	W	T	F	S	S	M	T
1	2	3	4	5	6	7	8	9	10	11	12	13	14	15	16	17	18	19	20	21	22	23	24	25	26	27	28	29	30	31

9 MONDAY

10 TUESDAY

World Mental Health Day

11 WEDNESDAY

12 THURSDAY

FRIDAY 13

SATURDAY 14

SUNDAY 15

NOTES

STRANGER THINGS

S	M	T	W	T	F	S	S	M	T	W	T	F	S	S	M	T	W	T	F	S	S	M	T	W	T	F	S	S	M	T
1	2	3	4	5	6	7	8	9	10	11	12	13	14	15	16	17	18	19	20	21	22	23	24	25	26	27	28	29	30	31

16 MONDAY

17 TUESDAY

18 WEDNESDAY

19 THURSDAY

FRIDAY 20

SATURDAY 21

SUNDAY 22

NOTES

S	M	T	W	T	F	S	S	M	T	W	T	F	S	S	M	T	W	T	F	S	S	M	T	W	T	F	S	S	M	T
1	2	3	4	5	6	7	8	9	10	11	12	13	14	15	16	17	18	19	20	21	22	23	24	25	26	27	28	29	30	31

23 MONDAY

24 TUESDAY

25 WEDNESDAY

26 THURSDAY

FRIDAY 27

SATURDAY 28

SUNDAY 29

Daylight Saving Time Ends

NOTES

STRANGER THINGS

S	M	T	W	T	F	S	S	M	T	W	T	F	S	S	M	T	W	T	F	S	S	M	T	W	T	F	S	S	M	T
1	2	3	4	5	6	7	8	9	10	11	12	13	14	15	16	17	18	19	20	21	22	23	24	25	26	27	28	29	30	31

THERE ARE SOME THINGS WORSE THAN GHOSTS

Max

NOVEMBER

NOTES

ST

30 MONDAY

31 TUESDAY Halloween

1 WEDNESDAY

2 THURSDAY

FRIDAY 3

SATURDAY 4

SUNDAY 5

Guy Fawkes Night

NOTES

STRANGER THINGS

M	T	W	T	F	S	S	M	T	W	T	F	S	S	M	T	W	T	F	S	S	M	T	W	T	F	S	S	M	T	W
16	17	18	19	20	21	22	23	24	25	26	27	28	29	30	31	1	2	3	4	5	6	7	8	9	10	11	12	13	14	15

6 MONDAY

7 TUESDAY

8 WEDNESDAY

9 THURSDAY

FRIDAY 10

SATURDAY 11

SUNDAY 12

DIWALI / REMEMBRANCE SUNDAY

NOTES

STRANGER THINGS

W	T	F	S	S	M	T	W	T	F	S	S	M	T	W	T	F	S	S	M	T	W	T	F	S	S	M	T	W	T
1	2	3	4	5	6	7	8	9	10	11	12	13	14	15	16	17	18	19	20	21	22	23	24	25	26	27	28	29	30

N

13 MONDAY

14 TUESDAY

15 WEDNESDAY

16 THURSDAY

FRIDAY 17

SATURDAY 18

SUNDAY 19

NOTES

STRANGER THINGS

W	T	F	S	S	M	T	W	T	F	S	S	M	T	W	T	F	S	S	M	T	W	T	F	S	S	M	T	W	T
1	2	3	4	5	6	7	8	9	10	11	12	13	14	15	16	17	18	19	20	21	22	23	24	25	26	27	28	29	30

N

20 MONDAY

21 TUESDAY

22 WEDNESDAY

23 THURSDAY

FRIDAY 24

SATURDAY 25

SUNDAY 26

NOTES

W	T	F	S	S	M	T	W	T	F	S	S	M	T	W	T	F	S	S	M	T	W	T	F	S	S	M	T	W	T
1	2	3	4	5	6	7	8	9	10	11	12	13	14	15	16	17	18	19	20	21	22	23	24	25	26	27	28	29	30

Hit Points
92
104
107
108
106
CLUB
107
106

DECEMBER

NOTES

STRANGER THINGS

27 MONDAY

28 TUESDAY

29 WEDNESDAY

30 THURSDAY

St. Andrew's Day

FRIDAY 1

SATURDAY 2

SUNDAY 3

NOTES

STRANGER THINGS

T	F	S	S	M	T	W	T	F	S	S	M	T	W	T	F	S	S	M	T	W	T	F	S	S	M	T	W	T	F
16	17	18	19	20	21	22	23	24	25	26	27	28	29	30	1	2	3	4	5	6	7	8	9	10	11	12	13	14	15

4 MONDAY

5 TUESDAY

6 WEDNESDAY

7 THURSDAY

FRIDAY 8

SATURDAY 9

SUNDAY 10

NOTES

STRANGER THINGS

F	S	S	M	T	W	T	F	S	S	M	T	W	T	F	S	S	M	T	W	T	F	S	S	M	T	W	T	F	S	S
1	2	3	4	5	6	7	8	9	10	11	12	13	14	15	16	17	18	19	20	21	22	23	24	25	26	27	28	29	30	31

11 MONDAY

12 TUESDAY

13 WEDNESDAY

14 THURSDAY

FRIDAY **15**

SATURDAY **16**

SUNDAY **17**

NOTES

F	S	S	M	T	W	T	F	S	S	M	T	W	T	F	S	S	M	T	W	T	F	S	S	M	T	W	T	F	S	S
1	2	3	4	5	6	7	8	9	10	11	12	13	14	15	16	17	18	19	20	21	22	23	24	25	26	27	28	29	30	31

18 MONDAY

19 TUESDAY

20 WEDNESDAY

21 THURSDAY

FRIDAY 22

SATURDAY 23

SUNDAY 24

NOTES

STRANGER THINGS

F	S	S	M	T	W	T	F	S	S	M	T	W	T	F	S	S	M	T	W	T	F	S	S	M	T	W	T	F	S	S
1	2	3	4	5	6	7	8	9	10	11	12	13	14	15	16	17	18	19	20	21	22	23	24	25	26	27	28	29	30	31

25 MONDAY Christmas Day

26 TUESDAY Boxing Day

27 WEDNESDAY

28 THURSDAY

FRIDAY 29

SATURDAY 30

SUNDAY 31

New Year's Eve

NOTES

STRANGER THINGS

F	S	S	M	T	W	T	F	S	S	M	T	W	T	F	S	S	M	T	W	T	F	S	S	M	T	W	T	F	S	S
1	2	3	4	5	6	7	8	9	10	11	12	13	14	15	16	17	18	19	20	21	22	23	24	25	26	27	28	29	30	31

D

PLANNER 2024

JANUARY		FEBRUARY		MARCH	
1	M	1	T	1	F
2	T	2	F	2	S
3	W	3	S	3	S
4	T	4	S	4	M
5	F	5	M	5	T
6	S	6	T	6	W
7	S	7	W	7	T
8	M	8	T	8	F
9	T	9	F	9	S
10	W	10	S	10	S
11	T	11	S	11	M
12	F	12	M	12	T
13	S	13	T	13	W
14	S	14	W	14	T
15	M	15	T	15	F
16	T	16	F	16	S
17	W	17	S	17	S
18	T	18	S	18	M
19	F	19	M	19	T
20	S	20	T	20	W
21	S	21	W	21	T
22	M	22	T	22	F
23	T	23	F	23	S
24	W	24	S	24	S
25	T	25	S	25	M
26	F	26	M	26	T
27	S	27	T	27	W
28	S	28	W	28	T
29	M	29	T	29	F
30	T			30	S
31	W			31	S

PLANNER 2024

APRIL		MAY		JUNE	
1	M	1	W	1	S
2	T	2	T	2	S
3	W	3	F	3	M
4	T	4	S	4	T
5	F	5	S	5	W
6	S	6	M	6	T
7	S	7	T	7	F
8	M	8	W	8	S
9	T	9	T	9	S
10	W	10	F	10	M
11	T	11	S	11	T
12	F	12	S	12	W
13	S	13	M	13	T
14	S	14	T	14	F
15	M	15	W	15	S
16	T	16	T	16	S
17	W	17	F	17	M
18	T	18	S	18	T
19	F	19	S	19	W
20	S	20	M	20	T
21	S	21	T	21	F
22	M	22	W	22	S
23	T	23	T	23	S
24	W	24	F	24	M
25	T	25	S	25	T
26	F	26	S	26	W
27	S	27	M	27	T
28	S	28	T	28	F
29	M	29	W	29	S
30	T	30	T	30	S
		31	F		

PLANNER 2024

JULY	AUGUST	SEPTEMBER
1 M	1 T	1 S
2 T	2 F	2 M
3 W	3 S	3 T
4 T	4 S	4 W
5 F	5 M	5 T
6 S	6 T	6 F
7 S	7 W	7 S
8 M	8 T	8 S
9 T	9 F	9 M
10 W	10 S	10 T
11 T	11 S	11 W
12 F	12 M	12 T
13 S	13 T	13 F
14 S	14 W	14 S
15 M	15 T	15 S
16 T	16 F	16 M
17 W	17 S	17 T
18 T	18 S	18 W
19 F	19 M	19 T
20 S	20 T	20 F
21 S	21 W	21 S
22 M	22 T	22 S
23 T	23 F	23 M
24 W	24 S	24 T
25 T	25 S	25 W
26 F	26 M	26 T
27 S	27 T	27 F
28 S	28 W	28 S
29 M	29 T	29 S
30 T	30 F	30 M
31 W	31 S	

OCTOBER		NOVEMBER		DECEMBER	
1	T	1	F	1	S
2	W	2	S	2	M
3	T	3	S	3	T
4	F	4	M	4	W
5	S	5	T	5	T
6	S	6	W	6	F
7	M	7	T	7	S
8	T	8	F	8	S
9	W	9	S	9	M
10	T	10	S	10	T
11	F	11	M	11	W
12	S	12	T	12	T
13	S	13	W	13	F
14	M	14	T	14	S
15	T	15	F	15	S
16	W	16	S	16	M
17	T	17	S	17	T
18	F	18	M	18	W
19	S	19	T	19	T
20	S	20	W	20	F
21	M	21	T	21	S
22	T	22	F	22	S
23	W	23	S	23	M
24	T	24	S	24	T
25	F	25	M	25	W
26	S	26	T	26	T
27	S	27	W	27	F
28	M	28	T	28	S
29	T	29	F	29	S
30	W	30	S	30	M
31	T			31	T

ADDRESS / PHONE NUMBERS

Name

Address

Telephone Mobile

Email

Name

Address

Telephone Mobile

Email

Name

Address

Telephone Mobile

Email

Name

Address

Telephone Mobile

Email

Name

Address

Telephone Mobile

Email

Name

Address

Telephone Mobile

Email

ADDRESS / PHONE NUMBERS

Name

Address

Telephone Mobile

Email

Name

Address

Telephone Mobile

Email

Name

Address

Telephone Mobile

Email

Name

Address

Telephone Mobile

Email

Name

Address

Telephone Mobile

Email

Name

Address

Telephone Mobile

Email

NOTES

NOTES

NOTES

NOTES